D1404482

TO NUMBER
s, and Hundreds

Graham A. Jones, and Kevin M. Hill

ISBN: 1-56911-986-4

Printed in the United States of America.

Table of Contents

• •

Introduction

Ways to Number focuses on extended place value activities for students in grades 2–3. This resource book features 44 hands-on activities to build understanding of 2- and 3-digit numbers and helps students develop general number sense. Each activity is presented as a game or cooperative problem-solving activity. Eighteen blackline masters of cards, game-boards, game mats, and other materials are included. Eight classic children's books are integrated into the hands-on activities. These books are listed on page 17.

The activities are classroom tested and designed to build on the skills students learned in *I Can Number the Ways* (Learning Resources, 1993). Following NCTM's *Curriculum and Evaluation Standards for School Mathematics*, the activities offer a creative approach to multidigit numbers and provide a solid foundation for students' future math experiences. The creative games and problem solving motivate students to get excited about math. This book provides experiences that can be repeated time and again to help children gain confidence in using numbers.

● ●

Learning to Work with Multidigit Numbers

Divided into two sections, *Ways to Number* features activities involving 2-digit numbers in one section and 3-digit numbers in the second section. Activity pages are labeled by skill in the lower righthand corner. Activities in both sections build on students' skills in the following five areas:

Counting. Children should be proficient at counting and counting on and back by 10s and 1s. These skills are crucial for understanding more advanced concepts. When students are able to count on and back with confidence, you can use a 100s Chart to introduce basic addition and subtraction.

Grouping. The activities in this book help children group and regroup numbers mentally or by using manipulatives. Students gain experience with 10s and 1s place value and later with 100s. Children then will be able to record multidigit numbers and solve problems using these numbers.

Estimating. *Ways to Number* offers many opportunities for students to practice making logical predictions. Encourage children to use grouping strategies to help them arrive at reasonable estimates. The activities also foster good number sense by asking students to explain their thinking.

Number Relationships. Recognizing and using number relationships is important for primary grade children to master because it prepares them for learning advanced thinking skills. In *Ways to Number*, children learn to relate to numbers by using the two phrases "more than" and "less than."

Partitioning. Students also are challenged to interpret numbers differently, that is, to partition, or break, numbers apart in various ways. For example, 43 can be 4 tens and 3 ones, or 3 tens and 13 ones. 43 also can be expressed as 23 + 20, 50 – 7, and in many other ways.

Activity Pages

Ideally, the lessons should be introduced when the teacher can work with students to model the activities. When children understand the directions, they can be paired or grouped to complete the activities. Each activity follows the same format, asking children to:

♦ **Think-Do** Children think about what they would do or say. Each child works with a partner to complete the activity and find a solution.

♦ **Tell-Share** Children tell or share their findings with classmates. The "Tell-Share" questions help the teacher extend children's thinking as a basis for whole-class wrap-up.

Teaching Notes

The Teaching Notes provide an overview and suggestions for using the activities with children. "Getting Ready" presents ideas for building important basic skills, so children can successfully participate in the activities. The "Using the Activities" section includes instructional hints related to the activities, and the "Wrap-Up" section offers ideas for extending the concepts covered.

Storing Materials

Children should keep math supplies at their desks so they are readily accessible. One simple, inexpensive way to store supplies is a "back-seater." Here's how to make one:

1) Cut a piece of heavy material (cloth, plastic, or canvas) about 20 inches in length and as wide as a desk chair.
2) Hem the material at top and bottom.
3) Fold down the top about 4 inches, so the bag can be hung over the chair.
4) Fold the bottom up about 15 to 18 inches from the bottom, to form a pocket.
5) Hem the sides and you're finished.

Hint: Store cubes in Ziploc freezer bags, ten 10-cube trains in each bag.

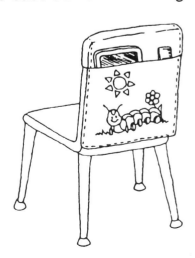

Teaching Notes
Section 1: Understanding and Using 2-Digit Numbers

Timeframe

Typically, activities should be introduced during the first semester of second grade. You can also use the activity pages as extension ideas with capable first grade students or as review in remedial programs. Note that even though these activities focus on 2-digit numbers, you can apply the same concepts to larger numbers.

Getting Ready

Extended counting experiences help children develop their understanding of place value. Children should be able to count and count on and back by 10s and 1s from any random number. Students will learn to use extended counting skills in the following situations:

- when they determine the number of objects in a large group (e.g., 10, 20, 30, 31, 32 — 32 beans);
- when they count on by 10s from a given number to determine the total: 45¢, here; 55, 65, 75¢ in all; and when they add or subtract on the 100s Chart.

Before beginning this section, assess children's ability to count and count on and back by 10s and 1s. A class 100s Chart or a transparency of a 100s Chart (Activity Master 7, p. 68) may be a useful reference source. Give children some "refresher" practice by having them perform these exercises:

- Start with 30 and keep counting by 10s.
- Start with 42 (or any other number less than 90) and count on by 10s; then count back by 10s and 1s.
- Start with 86 (or any other number greater than 10) and count back by 10s; count on by 10s and 1s.

To assess students' grasp of relationships between numbers, designate a number and ask children to:

- Tell a number that is a little more than that number.
- Tell a number that is a lot more; 1 less; a number that is 10 more/less.
- Tell a number that comes before or after the number; just before or just after.

Children might also be asked to tell a number that comes between two given numbers. You can help children confirm their answers by examining the 100s Chart or the page numbers of a book.

For students who lack confidence with the above *Getting Ready* tasks, focus first on activities coded "counting" and "number relationships" (see the lower right hand corner of the activity page). These activities will reinforce counting concepts for those who need it, and provide challenging review for other students.

Using the Activities

Note: For activities that require calculators, the keystrokes noted apply only to calculators with a "repeating equal" key.

Story Time 1: Show the Number *(page 18).* Read *Cloudy with a Chance of Meatballs,* and discuss it before beginning the activity. Then tell addition stories like the sample that involve children's using 3 or 4 different numbers. Write the numbers on the chalkboard for children's reference as you say them. Draw a rough picture illustration of each item you name.

Sample Story: Suppose (name of child in the class) lived in the town of Chew-and-Swallow. One morning (name of child) found 23 meatballs, 16 pancakes, and 34 hot dogs in the front yard.

In "Tell-Share," allow time for students to explain how they placed their counters. Students need to learn that grouping by 10s (a basic place value concept) makes counting "quicker" than grouping by 2s or 5s.

20, More or Less *(page 19).* Because the number 20 is relatively small, students may group by 2s or 5s instead of by 10s.

Low–High Five *(page 20).* Post a large 100s Chart upon which children can check their number sequences. (**Hint:** Keep the chart posted all year, as it will be a useful counting tool.) Students might also use book pages to help. As an extension, ask students to pick a card and challenge their partners to tell a number that comes before and after the number on the card; a number that is 10 more; 10 less....

Jigsaw: Find 50 *(page 21).* For "Tell-Share," write 6 random numbers on each grid of Activity Master 3. Children need to fill in the blanks and order the numbers 1 to 50. Ask children to cut the grids into 6 interesting pieces, then store them in an envelope. Later, they can write in the missing numbers on each puzzle piece and reassemble the grid. For each puzzle completed, children can autograph the envelope. Encourage students to trade their envelopes for an extra challenge.

10-Cube Count On *(page 25).* Before beginning this activity, demonstrate how to use a paper clip spinner. Ask students to place a pencil holding the paper clip at one end. Then have their partners spin the paper clip with a finger. If available, use 10-cube trains and loose, interlocking cubes or base 10 blocks instead of duplicating Activity Masters 7 and 8.

Story Time 2: How Many Did You Find? *(page 26).* Reread *Cloudy with a Chance of Meatballs.* Then tell addition stories like the sample that require students to add a 2-digit number and a multiple of 10. Write numbers on the chalkboard for children's reference as you say them.

> **Sample Story:** One morning (name of child in the class) ran out to collect food for breakfast. (Name of child) found 23 pancakes in the yard and 10 on the front patio. How many did (name of child) find that morning?

50, More or Less *(page 22).* Encourage children to group their beans so their partners can count them quickly and easily. Counters can be grouped by 2s or 5s, for example, but grouping by 10s makes checking quicker and easier.

10s Count *(page 23).* If individual calculators are not available to students, have them take turns using an overhead calculator. As an extension, have children take turns picking cards. Ask them to tell whether the number is closer to 0 or 100.

Jigsaw: Find 100 *(page 24).* You may want to provide each child with his or her own 100s Chart so they can use it for solving problems or checking their answers. Give children more practice by asking them to cover any number on the 100s Chart. Use the Peep Hole Card from Activity Master 8. Then ask students to count on by 10s or 1s as they move the card down or to the right.

Make 75 *(page 27).* Teachers need to encourage a variety of solutions. Some students may want to use a calculator to help or check. However, at this time, discourage the use of calculators. Stress the benefits of "thinking" rather than using machines. Students gain confidence by listening to others, so allow time to share ideas.

Make a Move *(page 28).* Prior to this activity and frequently throughout the year, provide opportunities for children to count on by 10s and 1s from any number on the 100s Chart. Continue to challenge students by asking them to count *back* by 10s and 1s.

Calculator Count On *(page 29)*. Use the calculator to reinforce skills in counting on. This activity also gives students practice in learning about calculators.

Story Time 3: On with the Show *(page 30)*. Read *Mr. Popper's Penguins*, and discuss it before beginning the activity. Then tell addition stories like the sample that focus on adding two 2-digit numbers. Write the numbers on the chalkboard for children's reference as you say them.

> **Sample Story:** On Friday evening, 36 people came to the Palace Theater to see Popper's Performing Penguins. On Saturday, another 42 people came to watch the show. How many people enjoyed these performances?

The Toy Factory *(page 31)*. This activity gives children practice in problem solving and in using place value to group by 10s.

Start with, End with 1 *(page 32)*. Give children directions for adding or subtracting multiples of 10, and have them move their counters on their 100s Charts. "Start with 34, add 20; add 30; subtract 40; add 10; subtract 20. What number do you end up with?" Repeat with different "start" numbers.

Make the string of directions shorter if students have difficulty following along. You can make this exercise more challenging by adding and subtracting 2-digit numbers that end in 1, 2, or 3.

Zoo Store *(page 33)*. For this activity, copy Activity Masters 12 and 13 on different colored card stock. Then cut each sheet into a deck of cards.

Start with, End with 2 *(page 34)*. As you begin this activity, write the equations for adding 10, then 11, to a number. Say "Start with 23 and add <u>10</u>. Now start with 23 and add <u>11</u>." Write: 23 + 10 = 33; so 23 + 11 = 34.

While you don't need to write equations for all sets, frequently write some to help students visualize their mental computations.

Ways to Make 100 *(page 35)*. If adequate supplies of interlocking cubes are available, put ten 10-cube trains in each Ziploc freezer bag, one bag for every two students. Without separating the cubes, have children partition the trains to show 10 + 90, 20 + 80, 30 + 70,...

Make 100 *(page 36).* For this activity, encourage students to work together to find as many sums of 100 as they think are possible. Note: The "100" card stands alone in this activity to "make 100."

Variation 1: Challenge students to use 2 or more cards to find combinations that "make 100."

Variation 2: Remove the "100" cards from the deck and find pairs that make 90. In this variation, the "90" card stands alone.

Cover the Number *(page 37).* If available, you may want to use 10-cube trains and loose cubes instead of the paper strips on Activity Master 8.

Story Time 4: How Many Oompa-Loompas? *(page 38).* Read *Charlie and the Chocolate Factory*, and discuss it before beginning the activity. When you and the students are ready, tell addition stories like the sample that involve problems with two 2-digit numbers. Write the numbers on the chalkboard as you say them for children's reference.

Sample Story: Charlie counted 29 Oompa-Loompas in one room of the factory and 48 more in another. About how many Oompa-Loompas did Charlie count?

For more advanced students: Tell 2-step story problems like the following: 100 Oompa-Loompas work in Mr. Wonka's factory each day. If Charlie saw 29 Oompa-Loompas in one room of the factory and 48 more in another, did he see all the Oompa-Loompas who were working that day? Tell how you know.

After each story, allow some time for children to compare their answers. Then call on several students to explain how they arrived at their estimates. If students give exact answers, work with the class to model an appropriate estimation strategy.

Story Time 5: Search for the Golden Ticket *(page 39)*. Review *Charlie and the Chocolate Factory,* and discuss it before beginning the activity. Tell addition stories like the sample that involve problems with two 2-digit numbers. Be sure to include some numbers that end in 7, 8, or 9. Write the numbers on the board for children's reference as you say them.

Ask students how they can solve the problems using different counting strategies. For example, for 29 + 34, some students might start with 29, count on 30, then 4 more. Others might start with 34, count on 30, and move back (subtract) 1.

Sample Story: In searching for a golden ticket, Violet opened 29 chocolate bars and Mike Teavee opened 34. How many chocolate bars did the two children open?

For more advanced students: Tell 2-step story problems like the following. Violet and Mike bought 100 chocolate bars to increase their chances for a Golden Ticket. By lunch time, Violet had opened 29 chocolate bars and Mike Teavee had opened 34, with no luck. How many chocolate bars were left to open?

Trade It ! *(page 40)*. This activity is similar to *Move It,* except that students *trade* 10s and 1s, instead of moving them from one number to the other. Explain to students

that they are "giving" and "taking" to make the numbers the same.

Your Choice *(page 41)*. If students compute exact answers to the problems, discuss how estimates help find solutions more quickly. In "Tell-Share," give children time to write down their answers, and then encourage them to explain their thinking.

Story Time 6: How Many Flowers to Pot? *(page 42)*. Read *Amelia Bedelia,* and discuss it before beginning the activity. Then tell subtraction stories like the sample that ask students to subtract a multiple of 10 from a 2-digit number. Write the numbers on the board for children's reference as you say them.

Encourage students to use different solution strategies. For example, for 54 – 20, some students might start with 54 and count back; others might start with 20 and count on to 54, figuring "how many more" are needed.

Sample Story: Amelia put out 54 flowers to pot. In no time at all, she had put 20 into cook pots. How many flowers did she still need to pot?

High–Low *(page 43).* Be sure students choose any 2-digit number greater than 50 as their "target sum" on the 100s Chart. In addition to helping students work with 2-digit numbers, this activity reinforces children's understanding of high–low relationships.

Story Time 7: Let's Make a Sponge Cake! *(page 44).* Read *Good Work, Amelia Bedelia,* and discuss it before beginning the activity. Then tell subtraction stories like the sample that involve subtracting two 2-digit numbers. Write the numbers on the chalkboard for children's reference as you say them.

> **Sample Story:** Amelia thought she would need 68 sponge pieces to make her sponge cake. Only 45 fit. About how many extras did she have?
>
> After each story, allow time for children to compare their estimates, then call on several students to explain their thinking. If students give exact answers, work with the class to model an appropriate estimation strategy. Discuss circumstances when estimates might be more appropriate.

Switch and Tell *(page 45).* This activity uses only digit cards numbered 1 to 9 on Activity Master 11. If children are uncertain about the more–less relationship between two numbers, they can use a 100s Chart or book pages to help or check.

Extend the "Tell-Share" section by asking children to color all numbers yellow that become greater when digits are reversed. Have them color all numbers orange that become less when digits are reversed. Help children discover that with numbers that stay the same when digits are reversed, such as 11, 22, and 33, they need to separate the two differently colored sets of cards.

Story Time 8 : At the Fair *(page 46).* Read *Charlotte's Web,* and discuss it before beginning the activity. Then tell subtraction stories like the sample that ask students to compare and subtract 2-digit numbers. At the beginning, select numbers for your story that are easy to use for estimates. Write the numbers on the chalkboard for children's reference as you say them.

After each story, allow time for children to compare their estimates, then call on several students to explain their thinking. If students give exact answers, work with the class to model an appropriate estimation strategy.

Sample Story: The first night Templeton found 54 great things to eat on the Fairgrounds. The second night he had plenty to eat with only 36 food bits. About how many more food bits did Templeton eat on the first night compared to the second?

Wrap-Up

An interesting summary activity for this section is *Two for 100.* Group children in pairs. Have each pair take a handful of beans and estimate how many they took. Then ask them to count the actual number. Together, they should decide on the total beans for the pair (by counting, mental calculation, or on paper).

After everyone finds a total, poll the class to determine which pairs "came close" to their estimates and which came closest to 100 without "going over." Call on several pairs to explain how they determined the total number of beans. Encourage students to show different solution strategies for finding the total number of beans.

Assessment. Determine how children arrive at their estimates. Ask them to explain how they calculate mentally, use a 100s Chart or a paper and pencil, or combine and count the beans. Note whether children group by 10s.

Teaching Notes
Section 2: Understanding and Using 3-Digit Numbers

Timeframe

Begin the activities in this section after children successfully complete the 2-digit problems in Section 1.

Getting Ready

Create a sense for "How Big is 100?" Ask each child to bring a bag of 100 items to school. Involve children in creating a 100s display by looping 10 bags with a long, brightly colored piece of yarn. Tape cards near each bag to help count the items within the loop: "100, 200, 300, 400, 500, 900, 1,000." Repeat with different colors of yarn, grouping up to ten bags together.

Involve the children in posing "what if" questions. For example, "What if I traded my collection of 100 trading cards for 100 of Nassar's, 100 of Timmy's, and 30 of T.J.'s things? How would you write the number of things I would have then?"

Using the Activities

Hunting 100s *(page 47).* Use the game-boards on Activity Master 15 to accompany this activity. Be sure children have a chance to play both boards.

More Than, Less Than *(page 48).* Extend this activity by using other numbers as benchmarks. More advanced students might explore numbers greater than 1000.

Two Bears on a Hill *(page 49).* Before beginning, give each pair of students Activity Masters 15 and 16. Ask students to fill in the missing numbers on the top of each hill. Model the activity by playing "teacher against the class," then allow time for students to play against each other.

Story Time 9: Help Save the Earth *(page 50).* Read *Brother Eagle, Sister Sky,* and discuss it before beginning the activity. Then tell sets of addition stories like the sample that involve problems with two 3-digit numbers. Write the numbers on the chalkboard for children's reference as you say them.

Notice how the numbers in the second story are related to those in the first. Children may recognize these number relationships and use them to mentally

figure out the answer to the second story problem.

> **Sample Story 1:** The brother and sister worked together. They planted 172 trees on the first day and 200 trees on the second. How many trees did they plant?

> **Sample Story 2:** The mother and father worked together. They planted 172 trees on the first day and 210 trees on the second. How many trees did they plant? Allow time for children to work together and share different solution strategies.

How Far Apart? *(page 51)*. To start, encourage students to put their markers on the same hill. Suggest 3-digit numbers that are multiples of 10. You may need to draw a Number Bank on the chalkboard to guide students in selecting "easier" numbers at first.

Which is Closer? *(page 52)*. This activity invites children to focus on the problem, "Which number is closer to a benchmark?" With practice, children discover number relationships and learn to compute figures mentally. Try repeating this activity with other benchmarks.

Story Time 10: Planting Seeds *(page 53)*. Review *Brother Eagle, Sister Sky*, and discuss it before beginning the activity. Then tell stories like the sample that involve problems with a 3-digit number. Write the numbers on the chalkboard for children's reference as you say them.

> **Sample Story:** The family had 385 sunflower seeds to plant.
>
> • If they planted 50 to a row, about how many rows would they have?
>
> • If they planted 25 to a row, about how many rows would they have?
>
> Allow time for children to work together and share different solution strategies.

Low–High Four *(page 54)*. To extend this activity, have children take turns picking a card, then have them challenge their partners to tell: the number before and after; a number that is a little more/less, and a number that is a lot more/less; the number that is 10 more/less, 100 more/less, and 50 more/less.

As an option, each child may pick a card and compare, add, or subtract the numbers.

Go for 1000 *(page 55)*. Prior to this activity, give children an opportunity to model 1000 in different ways. You may want to use base 10 blocks instead of paper for this activity.

Story Time 11: How Much in the Pot? *(page 56).* Read *Stone Soup,* and discuss it before beginning the activity. Then tell addition stories like the sample that involve problems with two 3-digit numbers. Write the numbers on the chalkboard for children's reference as you say them.

> **Sample Story:** The farmer's wife brought 225 carrots and 120 onions for the soup. How many vegetables did the farmer's wife bring?
>
> For more advanced students: Tell problems like the following one. Enough soup was in the pot to feed 600 people. If 325 men and 295 women wanted soup, was there enough soup to feed everyone? Tell how you know.
>
> Allow time for children to work together and share different solution strategies.

About How Much? (page 57). For this activity, use only the cards numbered 5 through 8 on Activity Master 11. If students are unable to predict the sums, work with them to develop estimation strategies.

Story Time 12: Put it in the Soup *(page 58).* Review *Stone Soup,* and discuss it before beginning the activity. Then tell subtraction stories like the sample that involve subtraction of 3-digit numbers

> **Sample Story:** The farmer's wife cut carrots into 690 coin-sized pieces. To help his wife, the farmer took 510 carrots from the pile and put them into the soup. How many carrot coins were still in the pile?
>
> Allow time for children to work together and share different solution strategies.

(each multiples of 10). Write the numbers on the chalkboard for children's reference as you say them.

Three in a Row *(page 59).* Instruct children to write the following numbers randomly on their game mats: 94, 130, 290, 790, 470, and 800. Then give clues like the following:

- 25 more than 225 (250)
- 19 more than 311 (330)
- 10 less than 800 (790)
- 5 more than 37 (42)
- 141 take away 11 (130)
- 900 − 50 − 50 (800)
- 82 + 12 (94)
- 13 less than 485 (472)
- more than 289, but less than 291 (290)

Repeat with other game mats and clues to help students learn about relationships between numbers. As a variation on this activity, group students in pairs, and have one partner show a number with trains or cubes. Then the other partner finds and marks it on the mat.

Make Them Match *(page 60).* This activity is similar to *Trade It* but uses 3 digits instead of 2. The following are solutions:

- 673 and 655: move one 10 and a 1 to show 664.
- 755 and 917: move one 100, two 10s and a 1 to show 836.
- 775 and 379: move two 100s and two 1s to show 577.
- 469 and 823: move two 100s, two 10s and three 1s to show 646.
- 671 and 437: move one 100, two 10s and three 1s to show 554.

Go for 777! *(page 61).* This book ends with an emphasis on mental computation, to give children more opportunities to increase their skills in thinking about and in using numbers. Encourage students to use base 10 materials or a calculator to check or help.

As in previous activities, allow time for creating an organized list, and ask about other ways to reach the target sum. Repeat this activity frequently, with different numbers, to build students' confidence in adding 3 digits.

Wrap-Up

As a summary activity for this section, challenge students with *Switch and See*. Ask students to find two 3-digit numbers, according to the following criteria:

- Pick a 3-digit number.
- Switch the first and last digits of the number.
- Add this new number to the original number, so the sum is between (500) and (600).

How many different numbers solve the problem? Discuss students' solution strategies by asking them to explain their reasoning. Repeat the activity with other target ranges.

Assessment. As children work, note whether they understand the problem. Ask them how they organize their thinking to find the solution and if they understand the relationships between numbers. Make a judgment about their overall number sense.

List of Books Used in the Activities

Atwater, Richard. (1938). *Mr. Popper's Penguins.* Boston: Little, Brown & Co.

Barrett, Judith. (1978). *Cloudy With a Chance of Meatballs.* New York: Atheneum.

Brown, Marcia. (1975). *Stone Soup.* New York: Charles Scribner's Sons.

Dahl, Roald. (1964). *Charlie and the Chocolate Factory.* New York: Bantam.

Jeffers, Susan. (1991). *Brother Eagle, Sister Sky.* New York: Dial Books.

Parish, Peggy. (1963). *Amelia Bedelia.* New York: Harper & Row.

Parish, Peggy. (1976). *Good Work, Amelia Bedelia.* New York: Greenwillow Books.

White, E. B. (1952). *Charlotte's Web.* New York: Harper & Row.

Story Time 1: Show the Number

Need: 40 counters per child, the book *Cloudy with a Chance of Meatballs.*

Can you place the counters for your partner
to count quickly and easily?

▲ Work with a partner and listen to the story.

▲ In secret, each partner picks one number and shows it with counters.

▲ Each partner tells the other partner's number.

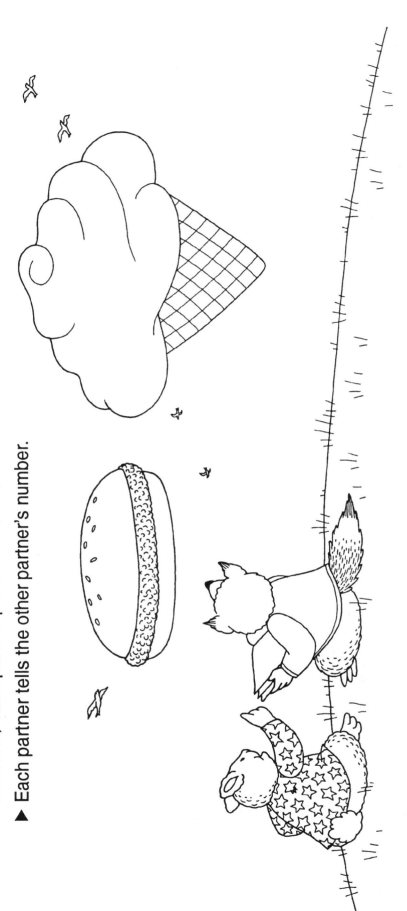

How did you place the counters so that your partner

could count them quickly and easily?

● ● ● 18 ● ● ●

20, More or Less

Need: Bag of 40 beans per pair.

How can you place the beans so your partner can count them *quickly and easily?*

▲ Take turns.

▲ Take a handful of beans from the bag. Try for 20.

▲ Count and write the number you took.

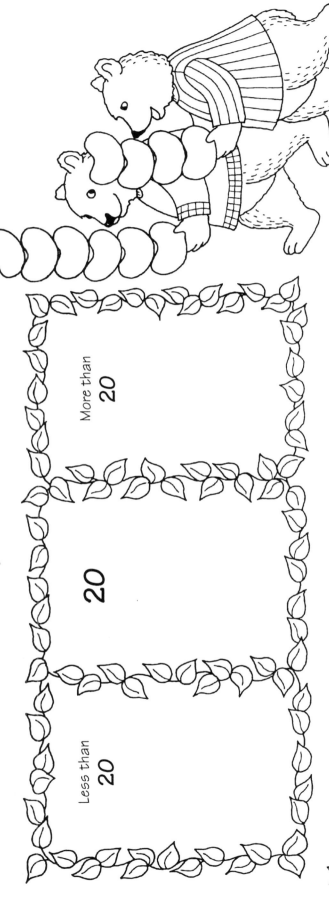

Less than
20

20

More than
20

Tell a number that you didn't pick that is less than 20.

Now tell one that is more than 20.

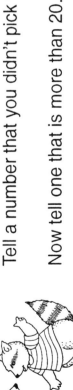

Ways to Number Ones, Tens, and Hundreds

Number Relationships

Low-High Five

Can you order numbers to 40?

▲ Mix the cards and put them face down.

▲ Take turns. Draw one card at a time, and put it on a card, in order from low to high.

▲ After you place a card, you cannot move it.

▲ If you cannot use a card, place it under the deck.

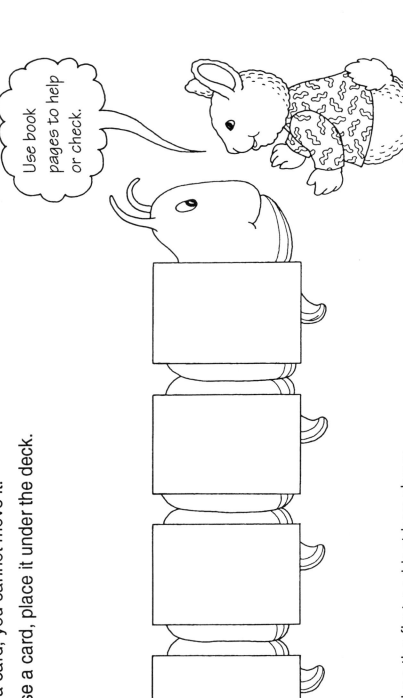

Use book pages to help or check.

Put a card on the first and last box above.
Partner tells 3 numbers that fall between the numbers on the cards.

Number Relationships

Jigsaw: Find 50

Can you put the puzzle together?

▲ Work together.

▲ Cut out the puzzle pieces on Activity Master 2.

▲ Put the pieces together.

▲ Fill in the missing numbers.

▲ Paste the puzzle pieces on one of the grids from Activity Master 3.

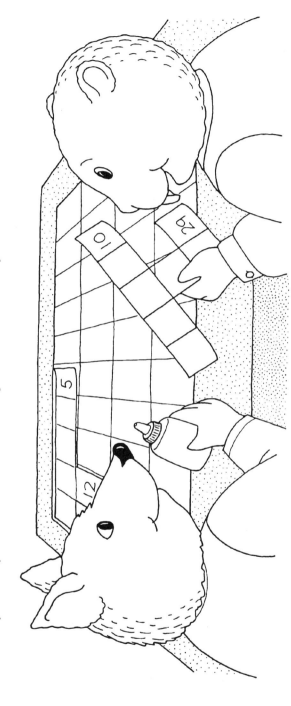

Make a different puzzle for your classmates.
Use numbers 1–50.

Ways to Number Ones, Tens, and Hundreds

Number Relationships and Counting

50, More or Less

Need: Bag of 70 beans per pair, book with 70 pages.

How can you place the beans so your partner can count them quickly and easily?

▲ Take turns.

▲ Take 2 handfuls of beans from the bag. Try for 50.

▲ Count and write the number you took.

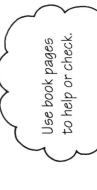

Use book pages to help or check.

Less than 50

50

More than 50

Tell a number that you didn't pick that is less than 50.

Now tell one that is more than 50.

Ways to Number Ones, Tens, and Hundreds

Number Relationships

10s Count

Can you fill in the missing 10s to 100?

▲ Mix the 10s cards and put them face down.

▲ Take turns. Draw a card and place it on a 🐾 so the cards are in order from low to high.

▲ If a 🐾 is already covered with a card, put your card back in the pile.

▲ Cover the elephant tracks to 100.

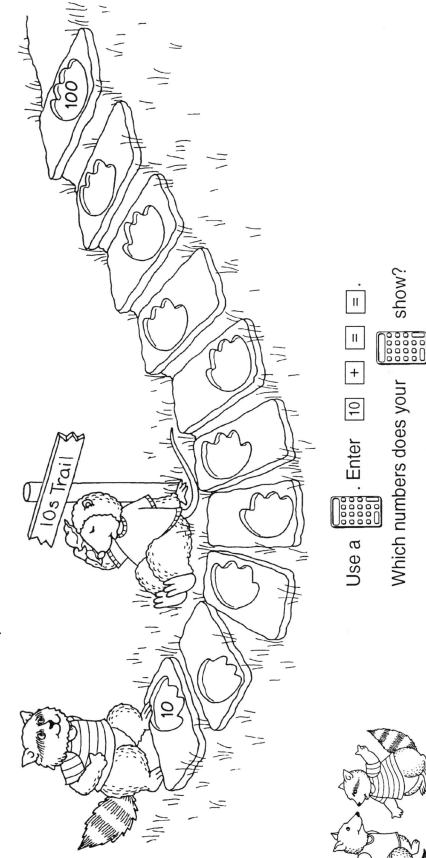

Use a 🖩 . Enter 10 + = = .

Which numbers does your 🖩 show?

••• 23 •••

Counting

Jigsaw: Find 100

Need: Activity Masters 5 and 6, scissors, and glue.

Can you put the puzzle together?

▲ Work together.

▲ Cut out the puzzle pieces.

▲ Put the pieces together.

▲ Fill in the missing numbers.

▲ Paste the puzzle pieces on the grid from Activity Master 6.

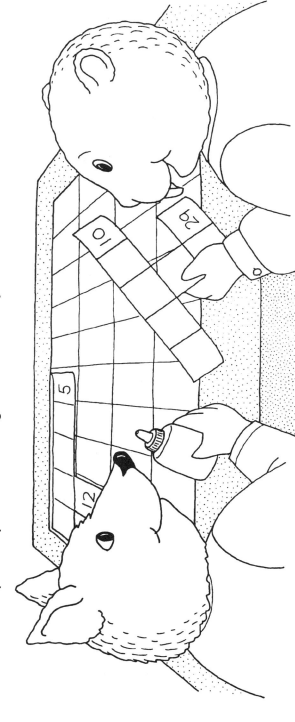

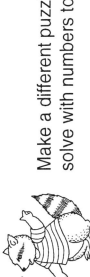

Make a different puzzle for your classmates to solve with numbers to 100.

Number Relationships and Counting

10-Cube Train Count On

Need: Activity Masters 7 and 8, paper clip.

Can you count on by 10s beginning with a 2-digit number?

▲ Take turns.

▲ Use  card. Put the card on a number less than 50.

▲ Show the number using 10-cube trains and 1s.

▲ Partner spins and takes 10-cube trains to make the number.

▲ Partner uses trains to count on from your number.

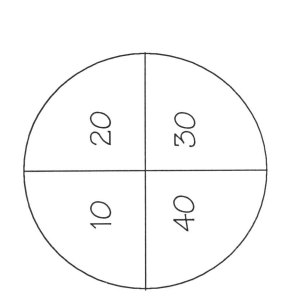

How many 10-cube trains do you need to make:

40?   60?   80?   100?

● ● ● 25 ● ● ●

Story Time 2: How Many Did You Find?

Need: Activity Masters 7 and 8, the book *Cloudy with a Chance of Meatballs.*

How many different ways can you solve the problem?

▲ Work with a partner and listen to the story.

▲ Use 10-cube trains and 1s to find the total.

▲ Record the number sentence on the back of this paper.

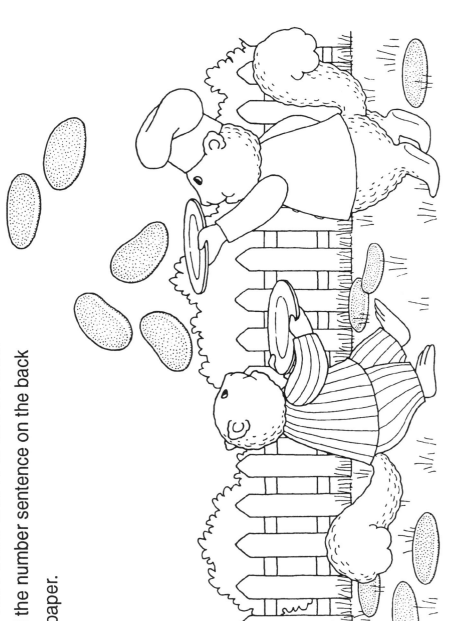

Show your partner how to use a 100s chart to solve the problems.

• • • 26 • • • •

Counting and Grouping

Make 75

Need: Activity Master 8, calculator, paper clip.

Use 10s and 1s or a calculator to help or check.

Which number do you add to a START number to end up with 75?

▲ Work together.

▲ Spin for a START number.

▲ Find 2 <u>different</u> ways to end up with 75.

▲ Record on the chart.

Different Ways for 75

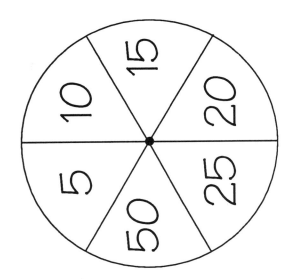

Spinner: 5, 10, 15, 20, 25, 50

Pick a number.

Show several different ways to end up with: 45   65   85

Ways to Number Ones, Tens and Hundreds

Partitioning

Make a Move

Can you count on by 10s and 1s?

On the 100s chart, put a marker on the ☐ 1 and take turns.

▶ Spin for 10s and 1s.

▶ Count aloud by 10s and 1s as you move your marker to 100.

1s

10s

Pick a start number: 23   36   48

Count on by 10s and 1s to 100.

• • • 28 • • •

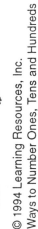

Ways to Number Ones, Tens and Hundreds

Counting

Calculator Count On

Can you count on by 10s and 1s using a  *?*

▲ Take turns.

▲ Enter a number less than 50 on your [calculator].

▲ Partner enters $+$ 10 $=$ $=$ ...to 100.

  and $+$ 1 $=$ $=$ ...to 100.

▲ Say the numbers as they appear on the display.

46, 56, 66, 76, 86, 96, 97, 98, 99, 100

Pick a number. Then tell what numbers the  would show when counting by 10s to 100 and 1s to 100.

© 1994 Learning Resources, Inc.
Ways to Number Ones, Tens and Hundreds

Counting

Story Time 3: On with the Show

How many different ways can the problem be solved?

Need: Activity Masters 7 and 8, the book *Mr. Popper's Penguins*.

▲ Work with a partner and listen to the penguin stories.

▲ Use 10-cube trains and 1s to find the total number of people.

▲ Record the number sentence on the back of this paper.

Create a penguin problem for your partner to solve.

Ways to Number Ones, Tens, and Hundreds

Counting and Grouping

Start with, End with

Need: Activity Master 7 and a counter for each child.

Can you add and subtract on the 100s Chart?

▶ Listen to the directions for moving the counter up or down on the 100s Chart.

"Add **30**..." that's down **3** rows.

"Subtract **20**..." that's up **2** rows.

Pick a START number on the 100s chart.

Partner picks an END number.

Tell how to get from one number to the other.

Counting

Toy Factory

How many toys can be made?

▲ Work together. Each caterpillar toy needs 10 wheels.

▲ How many toys can the factory make with each box of wheels?

▲ Record the number on the chart. Use 10-cube trains and 1s to help find the answer.

Number of Wheels	Number of Toys Made

How many toys can be made from the extra wheels?
In all, about how many toys can the factory make?
Tell how you know.

● ● ● 31 ● ● ●

Grouping

Zoo Store

Can you tell the total cost?

▲ Work together.

▲ Each partner mixes one deck of cards and spreads them out on the table, face up.

▲ Take turns.

— Pick one animal from each deck.

— Tell the total cost and record.

— Keep the cards if you are right.

How much is it?

Use 100s chart to help or check.

Toy Cost

Which 3 zoo animals together cost about $1.00?

Counting

Start with, End with

Can you use the 100s Chart to add 9, 10, or 11 to a number?

▲ Listen to the directions for moving the counter to add 9, 10, or 11 on the 100s Chart.

36+10=46, so 36+9 is 1 less (45).

36+10=46, so 36+11 is 1 more (47).

Pick a START number in the 100s chart; partner tells how to add: 29   39   51

● ● ● 34 ● ● ●

Ways to Number Ones, Tens and Hundreds

Counting

Need: Activity Master 7 and a counter for each child.

Ways to Make 100

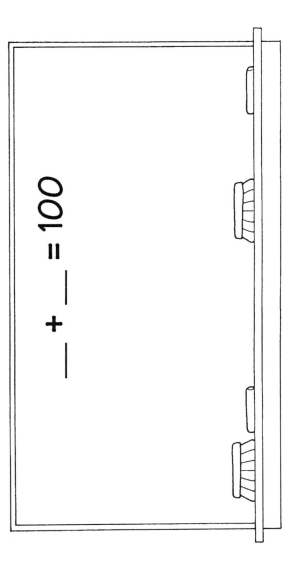

Need: Activity Masters 8 and 9 (flip side of 100 flat),10-cube trains.

How many ways can you make 100 with 10-cube trains?

▲ Turn a paper ⟨100⟩ over to the blank side and take turns.

▲ Put some paper 10-cube trains on the ⟨100⟩ and tell how many holes.

▲ Partner tells how many more holes will make 100.

(Use 10-cube trains to check.)

▲ Find all the ways and record.

___ + ___ = 100

What other numbers together will make 100?

Ways to Number Ones, Tens and Hundreds

••• 35 •••

Make 100

Which 2 numbers together make 100?

▲ Mix the 10s cards and place them in a pile, face down.

▲ Pick 4 cards and lay them in a row, face up.

▲ Take turns.

— Draw a card.

— Look for pairs of cards that add up to 100.

— Keep them.

— Put new cards in the empty spaces.

▲ Try to find all cards that together make 100.

80 20 70 50

Use the 5s deck. What pairs of cards added together make 100?

Cover the Number

Can you find and cover the number on the mat?

▲ Work with a partner.

▲ In secret, each partner picks a number from the mat and writes it.

▲ Each partner:

  — shows the number with 10-cube trains and 1s, then

  — trades one 10-cube train for ten 1s.

▲ Try to find and cover each other's number on the mat.

Cover the Number Mat

32	27	46	39	82	24
63	43	75	57	43	98

Pick a number: 26   33   42   56

Tell 2 ways to show it with 10-cube trains and 1s.

Ways to Number Ones, Tens, and Hundreds

Grouping and Partitioning

Story Time 4: How Many Oompa-Loompas?

Need: Counters, the book *Charlie and the Chocolate Factory.*

How many different ways can you estimate the answer?

▲ Work with a partner.

▲ Listen to the adventure in the chocolate factory.

▲ Mark your estimate with a counter.

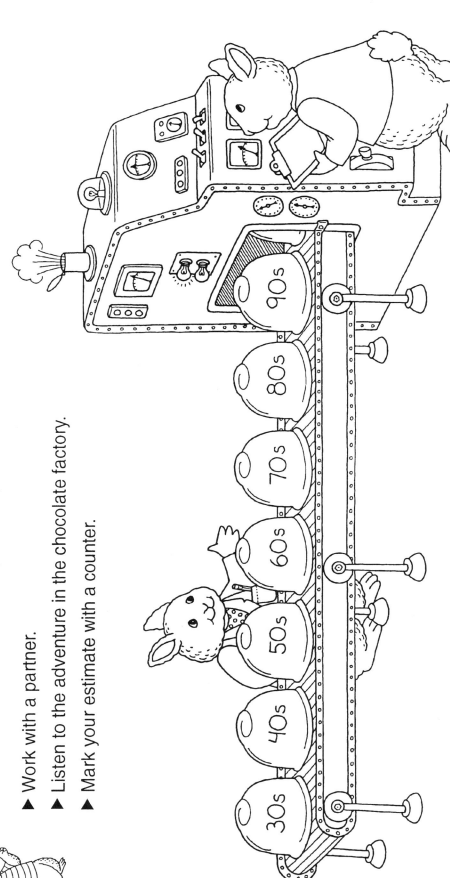

Tell how you decided on your estimate.

Grouping and Estimating

Story Time 5 : The Golden Ticket

Need: Calculator, Activity Master 7, the book *Charlie and the Chocolate Factory*.

How many different ways can you solve the problem?

▲ Listen to the story about the search for the golden ticket.

▲ Solve the problem in your head or on a 100s Chart.

▲ Partner uses a calculator to check.

Problem Solving in the Chocolate Factory

29+34

Pick a number: 65   75   85

Create a chocolate factory story for your partner to solve. Use your number as the answer.

Ways to Number Ones, Tens, and Hundreds

Counting and Grouping

Trade It

Can you trade 10-cube trains and 1s to make the numbers the same?

▲ Work together and pick a number pair from the Number Bank.

▲ Each partner shows one number with 10-cube trains and 1s.

▲ Trade 10s or 1s to end up with 2 numbers that are the same.

▲ Write the new number in the circle.

Number Bank

Number Pair		New Number
42, 28	→	◯
95, 59	→	◯
34, 72	→	◯
83, 67	→	◯
21, 87	→	◯
75, 51	→	◯

I have 42. I will give you one 10.

Yes, and I will give you three 1s. Then we'll both have 35.

For what other number pairs can you trade 10s or 1s to end up with 2 numbers that are the same?

Grouping and Partitioning

Your Choice

Need: Activity Master 12.

Can you work together to solve the problem?

▲ Pick a card.

▲ Find the animals that answer each question.

1. Which 2 zoo animals cost the most? The least?	2. Find 2 animals that cost •almost <u>80¢</u> •<u>almost 60¢</u>
3. Which 2 zoo animals cost about the same?	4. What can you buy: •with 90¢? •with 50¢?

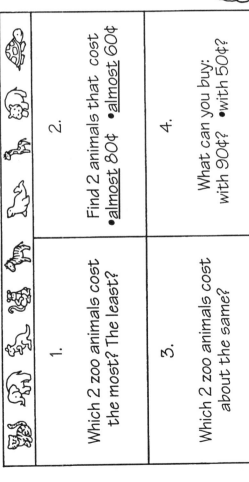

Choose one of the problems. Write about how you found the answer.

Ways to Number Ones, Tens, and Hundreds

Partitioning

Need: Activity Masters 7 and 8, the book *Amelia Bedelia*.

Story Time 6: How Many Flowers to Pot?

How many different ways can you solve the problem?

▲ Work with a partner and listen to the story about Amelia Bedelia's flowers.

▲ Use 10-cube trains and 1s to solve the problem.

▲ Record the number sentence below.

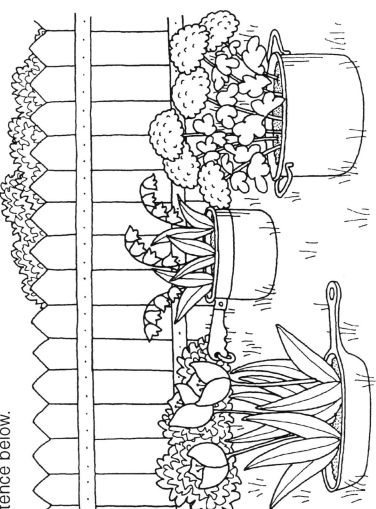

Show your partner how to use a 100s chart to solve the problem.

Counting and Grouping

High-Low

Can you pick 2 numbers that together make up the sum?

▲ Take turns.

▲ Pick a target sum from the 100s chart that is more than 50.

▲ Spin and tell 2 numbers that together make the target sum.

—If you spin "High," tell a high number.

—If you spin "Low," tell a low number.

High: I say 46.

Then I have to say 26, because 46 + 26 = 72.

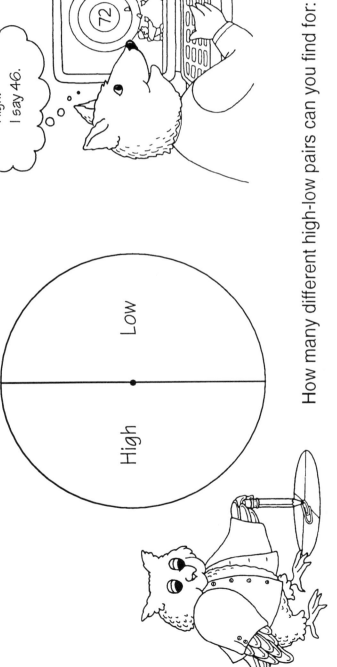

How many different high-low pairs can you find for:

99?   88?   77?

• • • 43 • • •

Partitioning

Need: Counters, the book *Amelia Bedelia*.

Story Time 7: Let's Make a Sponge Cake

How many different ways can you estimate the answer?

▲ Work with a partner.

▲ Listen to the stories about Amelia Bedelia.

▲ Mark your estimate with a counter.

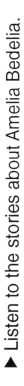

20s 30s 40s 50s 60s

Tell how you decided on your estimate.

Ways to Number Ones, Tens, and Hundreds

Grouping and Estimating

Switch and Tell

Is the sum more or less than the first?

Is it in the 30s, 40s, or 50s?

▲ Work together.

▲ Mix the cards and place them in a pile, face down.

▲ Each partner picks 2 cards to make a 2-digit number.

▲ Estimate the sum of both 2-digit numbers, and record it.

▲ Switch the digits of each number, and estimate the sum.

▲ Record the new sum.

▲ Is the 1st or 2nd sum greater? Circle it.

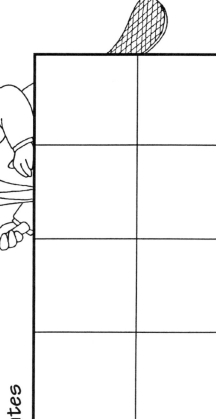

Sum Estimates

1st sum								
2nd sum								

When you switch the digits in the numbers on a 100s chart, which numbers:

• get bigger?

• get smaller?

• stay the same?

Number Relationships and Estimating

Story Time 8: At the Fair

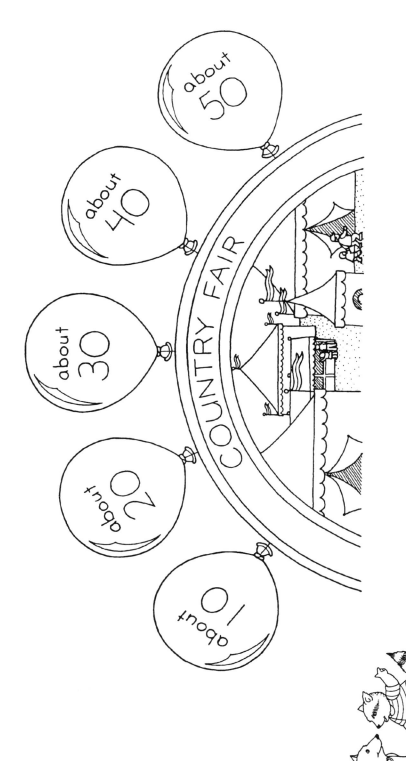

How many different ways can you estimate the answer?

▲ Work with a partner.

▲ Listen to what Wilbur's friends find at the fair.

▲ Use a counter to mark about how much more one number is than another.

Need: Counters, the book *Charlotte's Web*

Explain how you arrived at your estimate.

Ways to Number Ones, Tens, and Hundreds

Grouping and Estimating

Hunting 100s

Need: 2 counters, Activity Master 15, and a paper clip for spinner.

Can you count by 10s beyond 100?

▲ Put markers at 0 on the game board, then take turns.

▲ Spin and move that number of spaces. Count by 10s as you go.

▲ Partner tells what number could be added to your number to make the next 100.

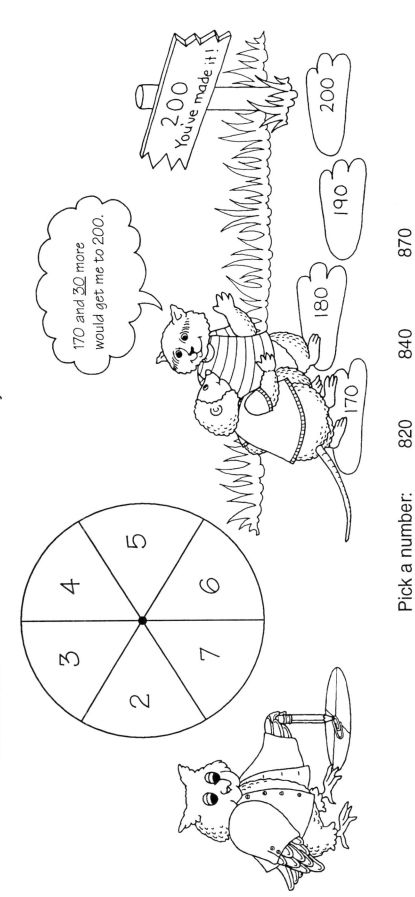

Pick a number: 820 840 870

Tell how many more the number is than 800. How many numbers are needed to make 900?

Ways to Number Ones, Tens, and Hundreds

Counting

Need: Activity Masters 8 and 9.

More than, Less than

Can you tell how much more a number is than 100?

How much less is it than 200?

▲ Take turns.

▲ Pick a number from the Number Bank. Tell how much more it is than 100.

▲ Partner tells how much less it is than 200.

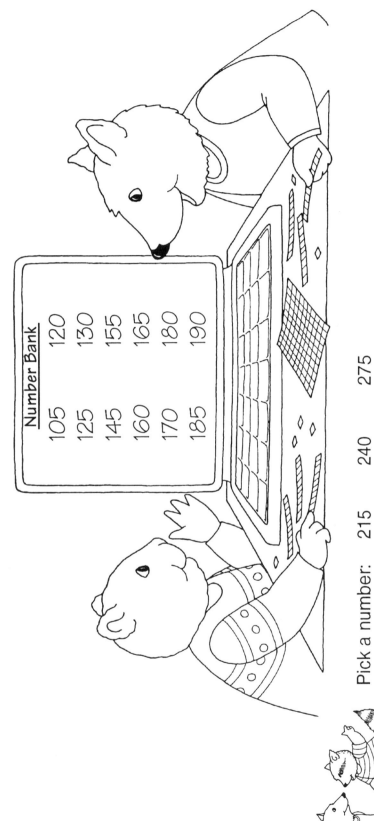

Number Bank	
105	120
125	130
145	155
160	165
170	180
185	190

Pick a number: 215   240   275

Tell how much more it is than 200. Then tell how much less it is than 300.

Ways to Number Ones, Tens, and Hundreds

Grouping and Partitioning

Two Bears on a Hill

Can you tell how far your bear is from 100?

▲ Work with a partner.

▲ Each partner chooses one counter. One partner is Black Bear; one is Brown Bear.

▲ Pick a number from your bear's chart.

▲ Find that number on the hill. Mark it with your counter.

▲ How far is each number from the bottom of a hill?

Brown Bear's Numbers

40	270	420
130	310	480
240	390	560

Black Bear's Numbers

30	260	450
120	340	530
170	410	580

Put the counters on a hill but not on the top.

Tell how far each bear is to the *top* of the hill.

Ways to Number Ones, Tens, and Hundreds

Counting

Story Time 9: Save the Earth

Need: Activity Masters 8 and 9, the book *Brother Eagle, Sister Sky*.

Can you count on to solve the problem?

▲ Work with a partner.

▲ Listen to the story about our Earth.

▲ Use 100s flats, 10-cube trains, and 1s to solve the problem.

▲ Record in a number sentence below.

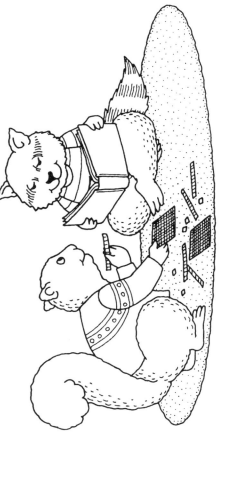

My number sentence:

Choose <u>one</u> number and show it with 100s flats, 10-cube trains, and 1s:

150   225   275

Show your partner how to use 100s flats to count: • 200 more   • 300 more

• 220 more   • 330 more

• • • 50 • • •

Ways to Number Ones, Tens, and Hundreds

Counting and Grouping

How Far Apart?

Can you tell how far one number is apart from another?

▲ Work together.

▲ Pick a marker. One partner is Black Bear; one is Brown Bear.

▲ Put the bears on a hill.

▲ Write the number for each and tell how far apart they are.

▲ Explain your thinking below.

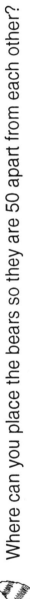

250

200

Where can you place the bears so they are 50 apart from each other?

How many different ways can you place them?

••• 51 •••

© 1994 Learning Resources, Inc.
Ways to Number Ones, Tens, and Hundreds

Grouping

Which is Closer?

Need: Activity Masters 8, 9, and 11.

Is the first or second number closer to 200?

▲ Work together. Mix the cards and place them in a pile, face down.

▲ Each partner picks 2 cards to complete a 3-digit number on the Number Board.

▲ Decide which number is closer to 200. Explain how you know.

▲ Hint: Use 100 , 10-cube trains, and 1s to help or check.

Number Board

Complete other 3-digit numbers.

About how far apart are they? Explain how you decided.

Number Relationships

Story Time 10: Planting Seeds

How many 50s are in a number?   How many 25s?

▲ Work with a partner.

▲ Listen to the numbers in the story.

▲ Tell your partner how many 50s there are.

▲ Partner tells you how many 25s there are.

▲ Hint: Use a 100s Chart to help or check.

Pick a number: 105   285   310   490

Tell about how many there are of: •50s   •25s

••• 53 •••

Low-High Four

Can you order 3-digit numbers?

▲ Mix the cards and place them in a pile, face down.

▲ Work together. Draw one card at a time and put it on

a ☐ , in order from low to high.

▲ After you place a card, you cannot move it.

▲ If you cannot use a card, place it under the deck.

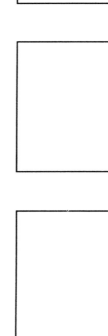

Put a card on the first and last ☐ .

Partner tells 2 numbers that fall between the numbers on the cards.

Ways to Number Ones, Tens, and Hundreds

Number Relationships

Go for 1000

Can you trade 10s and 100s to make 1000?

▲ Start with five 10-cube trains. Take turns.

▲ Spin and take that number of 10-cube trains.

▲ Try to keep as few trains as you can. Trade 10-cube trains for 100s flats when you can.

▲ Partner records the new number.

▲ Try to get to 1000 before other teams.

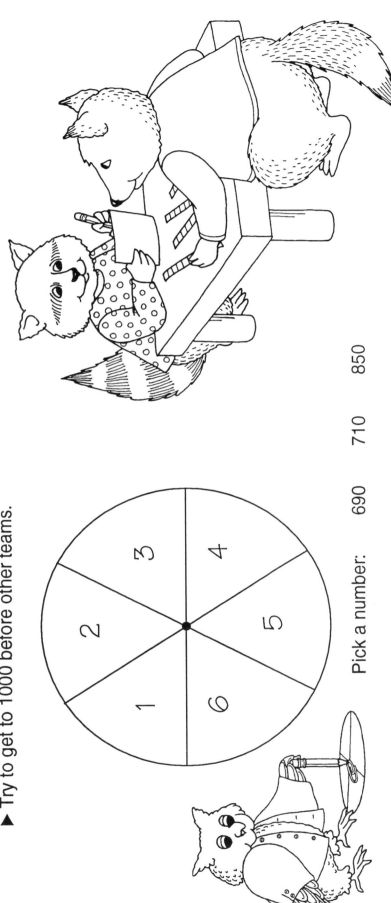

Pick a number: 690   710   850

Tell how many more you need to make 1000.

Ways to Number Ones, Tens, and Hundreds

Counting and Grouping

Story Time 11: How Much is in the Pot?

How many different ways can you solve the problem?

▲ Work with a partner.

▲ Listen to the story about the pot of soup.

▲ Figure out the problem.

▲ Record the number sentence below.

▲ Hint: Use a 100s chart and 10s and 1s to help or check.

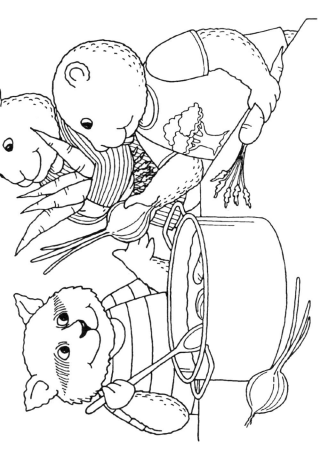

My number sentence:

Pick one: 445 + 525   365 + 225   145 +145 +145

Tell what you know without giving the answer.

Ways to Number Ones, Tens, and Hundreds

Counting and Grouping

About How Much?

Is the sum in the 600s, 700s, 800s, or 900s?

▲ Mix the cards (numbers 5-8 only) and place them in a pile face down.

▲ Work together.

▲ Each partner picks 2 cards to complete a 3-digit number in the Number Box.

▲ Tell whether the sum of the two numbers is in the 600s, 700s, 800s, or 900s.

▲ Record the number on a line at the right.

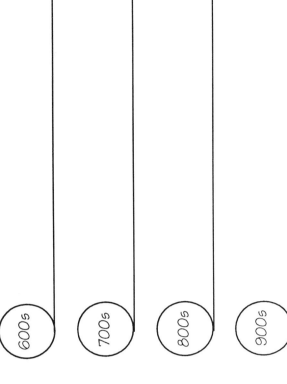

Number Box

		1
	1	

What other numbers have sums in the 600s? _____ 800s? _____

Use another piece of paper to make your own *long* list!

Ways to Number Ones, Tens, and Hundreds

Grouping and Estimating

Story Time 12: Put it in the Soup

Need: Activity Masters 7 and 8, the book *Stone Soup*.

How many ways can you solve the problem?

▲ Work with a partner.

▲ Listen to the story.

▲ Solve the problem. Use 100s chart and 10s and 1s to help or check.

▲ Record the number sentence below.

Create a problem that compares 2 numbers with an answer in the:

200s   300s   400s

Counting and Grouping

Three in a Row

Can you listen to the clues to find the number?

▲ Work together. Listen and write the numbers on the mat.

▲ As you solve the clues, cover the numbers with your counters.

▲ Try to get three in a row, across, down, or diagonally.

3 in a row!

Game Mat

	250	
330		
		42

Can you write other clues for the numbers on your mat?

Read them for your partner to guess.

Ways to Number Ones, Tens, and Hundreds

Number Relationships

Make Them Match

Need: Activity Masters 8 and 9.

Can you trade flats, trains, or 1s to make the numbers match?

▲ Work together.

▲ Pick a number pair from the Number Bank.

▲ Each partner shows one number with flats, trains, and 1s.

▲ Trade flats, trains, or 1s to end up with 2 numbers that match.

Number Bank

Number Pair		New Number
673, 655	→	◯
755, 917	→	◯
775, 379	→	◯
469, 823	→	◯
671, 437	→	◯

I'll give you one 10 if you'll give me one.

655

673

Then we'll both have 664.

For what other numbers can you trade your pieces to end up with 2 numbers that match?

Ways to Number Ones, Tens, and Hundreds

Grouping

Go for 777!

Need: Activity Masters 8 and 9, calculator (optional).

Can you add to a START number to end up with 777?

▲ Work together.

▲ Spin for a START number.

▲ Find 2 different ways to make 777.

▲ Record number sentences using different START numbers.

Hint: Use flats, trains, and 1s or a  to help.

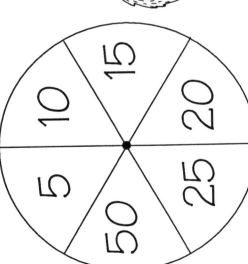

Different Ways to Make 777

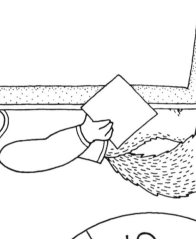

What other ways can you find to make 777? Make a long list!

Partitioning

Activity Master 1: Numbers to 40 (Low-High Five)

1	2	3	4	5	6	7	8	9	10
11	12	13	14	15	16	17	18	19	20
21	22	23	24	25	26	27	28	29	30
31	32	33	34	35	36	37	38	39	40

Activity Master 2: Jigsaw Pieces (Find 50)

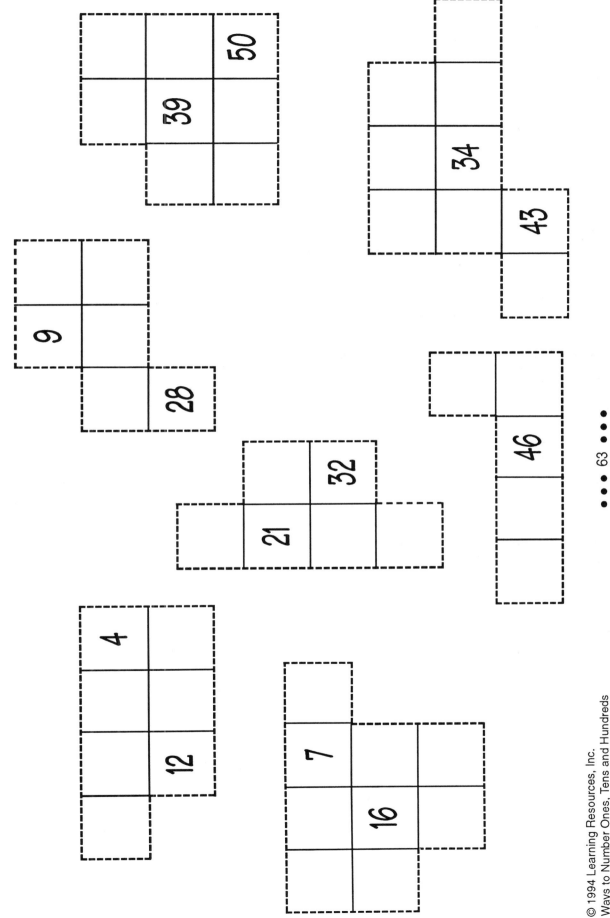

Activity
Master 3:
Blank Grids
(Jigsaw: Find 50)

• • • 64 • • • •

Activity Master 4: 10s Cards (10s Count)

10	10	10	20	20	20	30
30	30	40	40	40	50	50
60	60	60	70	70	70	80
80	80	90	90	90	100	100

Activity Master 5: Jigsaw Pieces (Find 100)

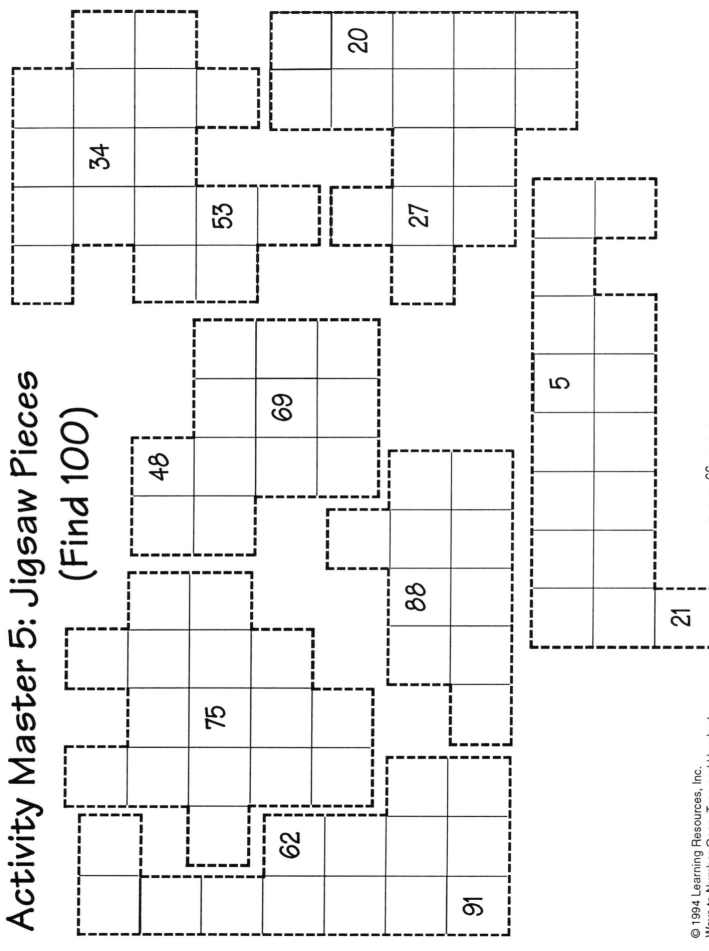

Activity
Master 6:
Blank Grid
(Jigsaw: Find 100)

Activity
Master 7:
100s Chart

1	2	3	4	5	6	7	8	9	10
11	12	13	14	15	16	17	18	19	20
21	22	23	24	25	26	27	28	29	30
31	32	33	34	35	36	37	38	39	40
41	42	43	44	45	46	47	48	49	50
51	52	53	54	55	56	57	58	59	60
61	62	63	64	65	66	67	68	69	70
71	72	73	74	75	76	77	78	79	80
81	82	83	84	85	86	87	88	89	90
91	92	93	94	95	96	97	98	99	100

Activity Master 8: 10-Cube Trains and 1s

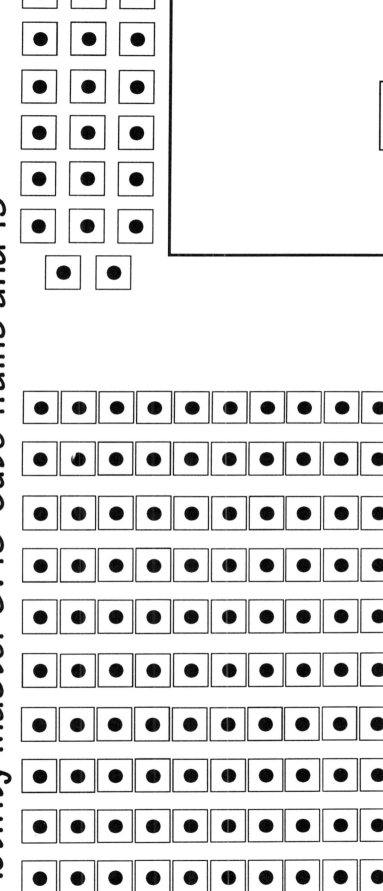

3x5 Peep Hole Card

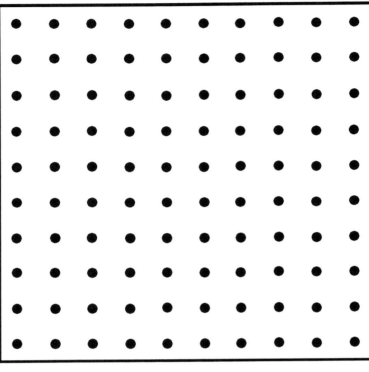

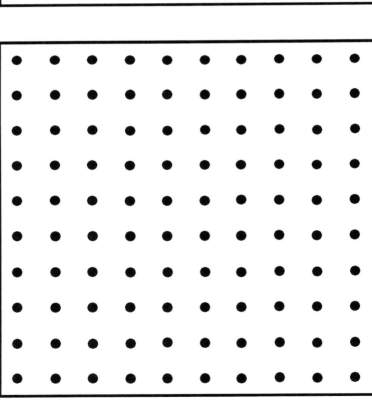

Ways to Number Ones, Tens and Hundreds

Activity Master 10: 25s and 50s

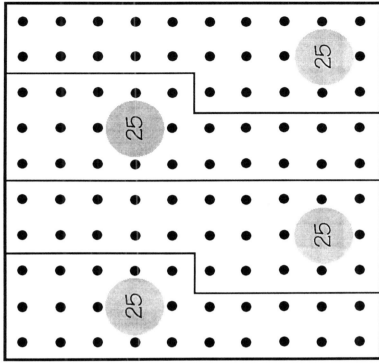

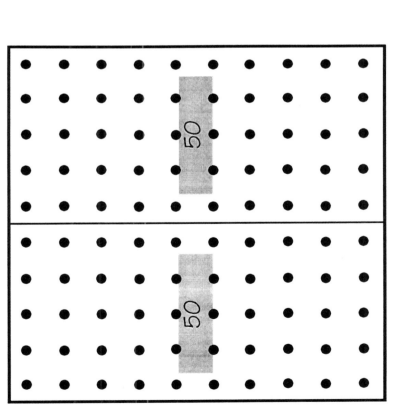

Ways to Number Ones, Tens and Hundreds

Activity Master 11: Digit Cards

0	1	2	3	4
5	6	7	8	9

0	1	2	3	4
5	6	7	8	9

Ways to Number Ones, Tens, and Hundreds